It's not easy to truly 'meet' ourselves. It takes courage and tenacity. But, there's one thing I know for sure: when you get courageous enough to do the work, really look inwardly and discover who you truly authentically are; the serendipity and synchronicity that unfold are truly magical.

– Lisa Messenger

create your
best life

2020, Collective Hub - Create Your Best Life Journal
All rights reserved. No part of this book may be reproduced in any form or
by any means, electronic or mechanical, including photocopying, recording
or by any information or retrieval, without prior permission in writing from
the publisher. Under the Australian Copyright Act 1968 (the Act), a maximum
of one chapter or 10 per cent of the book, whichever is the greater, may be
photocopied by any educational institution for its educational purposes
provided that the education institution (or the body that administers it) has
given a remuneration notice to Copyright Agency Limited (CAL) under the Act.
Any views and opinions expressed herein are strictly the author's own and do
not represent those of The Messenger Group. A CIP catalogue of this book is
available from the National Library of Australia.

ISBN 978-0-6485872-1-7
First published in 2020 by The Messenger Group Pty Ltd
Project management: @em.lystudio
Copy writing: @em.lystudio & Emily Ditchburn
Proofreading and sub editing: Emily Ditchburn & Victoria Kingsbury
Creative direction and design: @em.lystudio

Distribution enquiries: Lisa Messenger, lisam@collectivehub.com
This is proudly a Collective Hub product, collectivehub.com

create your
best life

EVERYTHING YOU
NEED TO ACHIEVE
YOUR DREAM LIFE

COLLECTIVE HUB
journal

slow down,
recharge.

live your best life

introduc-
tion

my fabulous team
and I have created
a beautiful,
nurturing space
within these pages
to guide, support
and hold you as
you fill it out.

This journal is dedicated to living **your best life**. It's something I wish I'd had access to early in my career, when I was navigating who I really was. At that point in my life, I was working out my purpose and trying to find the tools to unshackle myself from my negative traits and things from my past that were holding me back – challenges I think a lot of people can relate to.

My fabulous team and I have created a **beautiful, nurturing space** within these pages **to guide, support and hold you** as you fill it out. We want to help you develop a clear vision of what your ideal life looks like, then give you the tools to achieve it.

There are **no rules** in this space. There is no right or wrong way or order in which to fill it out. You can start from the back, work forwards, or start in the middle. You can write within the lines or go crazy and scribble, doodle and draw all over it. **Your life, your way**. We're merely here to guide you.

It's not easy to truly 'meet' ourselves. It takes courage and tenacity. But, there's one thing I know for sure: when you get courageous enough to do the work, really look inwardly and discover who you **truly authentically are**; the serendipity and synchronicity that unfold are truly magical.

So **thank you for being brave**. For wanting to dig deep and find out who you are and what you really want in life. We look forward to journeying with you. Feel free to DM me anytime @lisamessenger or my team @collectivehub and we'll support you as best we can along the way.

Big love,
Lisa and the Collective Hub team xx

@lisamessenger @collectivehub

contents

SET YOURSELF UP FOR SUCCESS

I love me, because...

_____
_____
_____
_____
_____
_____
_____
_____
_____
_____
_____
_____
_____
_____

YOU ARE IN CHARGE NOW

section one

all about you

〜〜〜〜〜〜〜〜〜〜〜〜〜〜〜

> **"**
>
> *Get into the habit of asking yourself: "Does this support the life I'm trying to create?"*
>
> — Unknown
>
> **"**

All about you

Living your dream life starts by knowing exactly who you are and what you want. These are the foundations that will lead you on the path to achieve your ultimate best life. Once you embrace your true self, set your goals and know your ambitions, your **best life** will follow naturally. We aren't saying it's easy, and there certainly will be obstacles, but you have to start somewhere, and that somewhere is **here, right now, in this journal**. Let us introduce you, **to you.**

So, who are **you?**

_____
_____
_____
_____
_____
_____
_____
_____
_____
_____
_____
_____
_____
_____
_____
_____
_____
_____
_____
_____
_____
_____
_____
_____
_____

What matters to you most? Why?

_____
_____
_____
_____
_____
_____
_____
_____
_____
_____
_____
_____
_____
_____
_____
_____
_____
_____
_____
_____
_____
_____
_____
_____
_____
_____

What are your interests/passions? Why?

_____
_____
_____
_____
_____
_____
_____
_____
_____
_____
_____
_____
_____
_____
_____
_____
_____
_____
_____
_____
_____
_____
_____
_____
_____
_____
_____
_____

What is your dream job? Why?

_____
_____
_____
_____
_____
_____
_____
_____
_____
_____
_____
_____
_____
_____
_____
_____
_____
_____
_____
_____
_____
_____
_____
_____
_____
_____

What are your health and wellbeing goals? Why?

_____
_____
_____
_____
_____
_____
_____
_____
_____
_____
_____
_____
_____
_____
_____
_____
_____
_____
_____
_____
_____
_____
_____
_____

What are your goals in finance/money? Why?

_____
_____
_____
_____
_____
_____
_____
_____
_____
_____
_____
_____
_____
_____
_____
_____
_____
_____
_____
_____
_____
_____
_____
_____
_____
_____

CREATE YOUR BEST LIFE

What are your goals for fitness and moving your body? Why?

_____

_____

_____

_____

_____

_____

_____

_____

_____

_____

_____

_____

_____

_____

_____

_____

_____

_____

_____

_____

_____

_____

_____

_____

_____

Where do you want to travel? Why?

_____
_____
_____
_____
_____
_____
_____
_____
_____
_____
_____
_____
_____
_____
_____
_____
_____
_____
_____
_____
_____
_____
_____
_____
_____
_____

What are your dreams for your friends and family? Why?

_____

_____

_____

_____

_____

_____

_____

_____

_____

_____

_____

_____

_____

_____

_____

_____

_____

_____

_____

_____

_____

_____

_____

_____

Use this space to write down more thoughts, goals and ambitions you may have:

_____
_____
_____
_____
_____
_____
_____
_____
_____
_____
_____
_____
_____
_____
_____
_____
_____
_____
_____
_____
_____
_____
_____
_____
_____

_____

_____

_____

_____

_____

_____

_____

_____

_____

_____

_____

_____

_____

_____

_____

_____

_____

_____

_____

In one sentence, write down your biggest, most important dream:

_____

_____

_____

_____

it's not what life throws at us, it's how we handle it.

learn.
grow.
come back
stronger
than ever.

@collectivehub

Notes:

CREATE YOUR BEST LIFE

Notes:

_____
_____
_____
_____
_____
_____
_____
_____
_____
_____
_____
_____
_____
_____
_____
_____
_____
_____
_____
_____
_____
_____
_____
_____
_____
_____
_____
_____

travel, be inspired

section two

setting up for success

> There is only one thing that makes a dream impossible to achieve: the fear of failure.
>
> — Paulo Coelho

Setting up for success

You'll already know there are a whole lot of aspects that come into living your best life. It's often difficult and overwhelming to try to juggle everything at once. Take a moment to section out your life and **focus** on the things **that mean the most to you**, then break those down into smaller tasks. The simplest things are sometimes the **most important** and the more you practise these, the faster they become second nature. **Routines and rituals** can be the difference between achieving a goal and watching it slip away. What you stick at, day after day, week after week, month after month and even year after year, will eventually **flourish**.

Start with smaller things, like moving your body every day, or drinking more water. The more **self-care** you practise, the better you'll feel and the more driven, motivated and focused you'll be to **achieve** that one end goal (or lots of smaller ones!).

Use this space to break down your dream life into sections and decide what areas you'd like to focus on first.

Here's an example:

Happiness
- Make time for family every Sunday
- Exercise four days a week
- Get eight hours of sleep every night

Now it's your turn
(think career, health, friends/family, money, fitness and more):

_____
_____
_____
_____
_____
_____
_____
_____
_____
_____
_____
_____

CREATE YOUR BEST LIFE

learn to hone your gut and intuition and focus on what you really want.

write it down.
visualise it.
draw it.

**and be then
be completely
in awe by the
synchronicity and
serendipity of what
starts to unfold.**

We've mapped out a few of our favourite routines and rituals that we live by, to help you on your way to feeling more accomplished than ever.

morning routine

~~~~~~~~~~~~~~~

every day is a new beginning and a wonderful opportunity to start it out the right way. don't be fooled – a solid morning routine might just be the best thing you ever do. use the next few pages to map out some morning routines, one that you think you can achieve tomorrow and then your ultimate dream routine that you'd like to achieve over the coming months.

realistic morning routine

5 AM

6 AM

7 AM

8 AM

9 AM

10 AM

11 AM

NOON

ultimate morning routine

5 AM

6 AM

7 AM

8 AM

9 AM

10 AM

11 AM

NOON

tomorrow's ideal morning routine

5 AM

6 AM

7 AM

8 AM

9 AM

10 AM

11 AM

NOON

| 5 AM |
| 6 AM |
| 7 AM |
| 8 AM |
| 9 AM |
| 10 AM |
| 11 AM |
| NOON |

> Give every day the chance
> to become the most
> beautiful day of your life.
>
> — Mark Twain

Exercise

We all know the importance of exercise and moving your body. Whether it's hitting 10,000 steps a day, going for a jog twice a week, or even just a 20-minute stretching session, try to move in some way every day of the week. We're not talking about major sweat sessions (although these are also encouraged), but just giving your body what it deserves – to be nourished by movement! Write down how you will move your body each day of the week, when you'll do it and the reasons why.

Monday

What will you do? _____

Why? _____

_____

Tuesday

What will you do? _____

Why? _____

_____

Wednesday

What will you do? _____

Why? _____

_____

Thursday

What will you do? _____

Why? _____

_____

_____

Friday
What will you do? _____
Why? _____
_____

Saturday
What will you do? _____
Why? _____
_____

Sunday
What will you do? _____
Why? _____
_____

Week in reflection
Jot down some notes about how you felt with the introduction of
more movement. What would you like to implement into your routine
every week and how will you keep yourself accountable?

_____
_____
_____
_____
_____
_____
_____
_____
_____

Nutrition

Health should always be your on top of your priorities list. It's the fundamental reason we are able to function. The better we look after our health, the more we should be able to focus and achieve. If you don't have your health, well – no need to say more!

List all the areas you could improve your nutrition and diet, then next to it, write out how you will change this:

_____   _____
_____   _____
_____   _____
_____   _____
_____   _____
_____   _____
_____   _____
_____   _____
_____   _____
_____   _____
_____   _____
_____   _____
_____   _____
_____   _____
_____   _____
_____   _____
_____   _____

why do you love
your favourite foods
so much!

_____
_____
_____

list your top 5 favourite treats:

_____
_____
_____
_____
_____

**when will you allow
yourself to enjoy
these treats?**

_____
_____
_____

lists and planning

there's only so much your brain can contain, and in today's fast-paced way of life, your brain is constantly overstimulated. sooner or later, you'll forget something important (we've all been there). make lists and make them every day. implement this into your morning routine before you delve headfirst into your working day. write up your to-do list and plan which items you'll tackle in the morning, during lunch, in the afternoon and finally the evening. keep on track and tick things off once you've completed them.

to-do list

date:

_____   _____
_____   _____
_____   _____
_____   _____
_____   _____
_____   _____
_____   _____
_____   _____

My daily goal: _____

My daily gratitude: _____
_____
_____

My daily checklist:
○ Moved my body   ○ _____
○ Eaten well   ○ _____
○ Had at least 2L of water ○ _____
○ Achieved my daily goal   ○ _____

to-do list

date:

_____

_____

_____

_____

_____

_____

_____

_____

My daily goal: _____
_____

My daily gratitude: _____
_____

My daily checklist:
○ Moved my body
○ Eaten well
○ Had at least 2L of water
○ Achieved my daily goal

○ _____
○ _____
○ _____
○ _____

to-do list

date:

_____

My daily goal: _____

My daily gratitude: _____

My daily checklist:
- ⭕ Moved my body
- ⭕ Eaten well
- ⭕ Had at least 2L of water
- ⭕ Achieved my daily goal

- ⭕ _____
- ⭕ _____
- ⭕ _____
- ⭕ _____

to-do list

date:

_____

_____

_____

_____

_____

_____

_____

_____

My daily goal: _____

My daily gratitude: _____

My daily checklist:
- ○ Moved my body
- ○ Eaten well
- ○ Had at least 2L of water
- ○ Achieved my daily goal

- ○ _____
- ○ _____
- ○ _____
- ○ _____

to-do list

date:

_____

_____

_____

_____

_____

_____

_____

_____

_____

_____

_____

My daily goal: _____

_____

My daily gratitude: _____

_____

My daily checklist:
- ◯ Moved my body
- ◯ Eaten well
- ◯ Had at least 2L of water
- ◯ Achieved my daily goal

- ◯ _____
- ◯ _____
- ◯ _____
- ◯ _____

to-do list

date: _____

_____   _____
_____   _____
_____   _____
_____   _____
_____   _____
_____   _____
_____   _____
_____   _____

My daily goal: _____
_____

My daily gratitude: _____
_____
_____

My daily checklist:
○ Moved my body   ○ _____
○ Eaten well   ○ _____
○ Had at least 2L of water   ○ _____
○ Achieved my daily goal   ○ _____

to-do list

date:

_____ _____
_____ _____
_____ _____
_____ _____
_____ _____
_____ _____
_____ _____
_____ _____

My daily goal: _____
_____

My daily gratitude: _____
_____
_____

My daily checklist:
◯ Moved my body   ◯ _____
◯ Eaten well   ◯ _____
◯ Had at least 2L of water ◯ _____
◯ Achieved my daily goal   ◯ _____

to-do list

date: _____

_____   _____
_____   _____
_____   _____
_____   _____
_____   _____
_____   _____
_____   _____
_____   _____

My daily goal: _____
_____

My daily gratitude: _____
_____

My daily checklist:

◯ Moved my body
◯ Eaten well
◯ Had at least 2L of water
◯ Achieved my daily goal

◯ _____
◯ _____
◯ _____
◯ _____

to-do list

date:

_____

My daily goal: _____

My daily gratitude: _____

My daily checklist:
- ◯ Moved my body
- ◯ Eaten well
- ◯ Had at least 2L of water
- ◯ Achieved my daily goal

◯ _____
◯ _____
◯ _____
◯ _____

Time for yourself/rest and recovery

Sometimes we all get a little overwhelmed, stressed or just a bit down. If and when you notice a change in yourself, find out why you're feeling this way and take a moment to process your true thoughts. **What are some ways you can help yourself through this?** Maybe it's reading a book, taking the afternoon off work, swimming in the ocean or simply sitting down with a cup of tea. Sometimes you might need a pampering session and indulge in a massage or facial, and other times it might be taking a trip overseas and just going off grid for a week or two. **Whatever it is, make the time for it.** Write down all the ways you like to take time out.

_____

_____

_____

_____

_____

_____

_____

_____

_____

_____

_____

_____

_____

_____

_____

_____

_____

_____

Set up your finances correctly/have a budget

Money, money, money. We wish it grew on trees! There are so many great tricks you can implement to save money without even noticing it. Try rounding up **every transaction**, or putting an auto-pay of x amount of dollars every week right **into your savings** account. Spend an hour or so every week on your finances and work out exactly where/how/what you're spending. List some ways you can tidy up your accounts and write down all your **money goals** for the future.

_____

_____

_____

_____

_____

_____

_____

_____

_____

_____

_____

_____

_____

_____

_____

_____

_____

_____

my financial goals

one

_____

_____

_____

two

_____

_____

_____

three

_____

_____

_____

five

_____

_____

_____

four

_____

_____

_____

six

_____

_____

_____

seven

_____

_____

_____

eight

_____

_____

_____

nine

_____

_____

_____

ten

_____

_____

let's all remember the value in taking risks, in standing on the edge of something, on choosing to go against the grain.

pull away from
the ordinary
to find your
delight.

Sleep hygiene

How many hours of sleep do you need to be your best self? As the old saying goes, sleep is the **best medicine**. Find your magic number and work toward achieving this every single night – yes, **even on weekends!** If you struggle with sleep, try switching off screens up to an hour before you get into bed. Drink herbal tea, have a bath, light a candle and get yourself into **sleep mode**. If your head is still buzzing with thoughts, take out a pen and paper and journal everything that's on your mind. Get it out of your head and say goodnight to it.

Spend a moment to write about how you can improve your sleep routine and how you'll begin implementing these things regularly:

_____

_____

_____

_____

_____

_____

_____

_____

_____

_____

_____

_____

_____

_____

_____

_____

_____

track your sleep

monday

hours: _____

quality: _____

wake up mood:

😃 😍 😐 😣 😠

tuesday

hours: _____

quality: _____

wake up mood:

😃 😍 😐 😦 😐

wednesday

hours: _____

quality: _____

wake up mood:

😃 😍 😐 😣 😠

thursday

hours: _____

quality: _____

wake up mood:

😃 😍 😐 😦 😐

friday

hours: _____

quality: _____

wake up mood:

😃 😍 😐 😦 😠

saturday

hours: _____

quality: _____

wake up mood:

😃 😍 😐 😦 😐

sunday

hours: _____

quality: _____

wake up mood:

😃 😍 😐 😦 😐

rate your week!

/ 10

😃 😍 😐 😦 😐

monday

hours: _____

quality: _____

wake up mood:

😃 😊 😐 🙁 😠

tuesday

hours: _____

quality: _____

wake up mood:

😃 😊 😐 🙁 😠

wednesday

hours: _____

quality: _____

wake up mood:

😃 😊 😐 🙁 😠

thursday

hours: _____

quality: _____

wake up mood:

😃 😊 😐 🙁 😠

friday

hours: _____

quality: _____

wake up mood:

😃 😊 😐 🙁 😠

saturday

hours: _____

quality: _____

wake up mood:

😃 😊 😐 🙁 😠

sunday

hours: _____

quality: _____

wake up mood:

😃 😊 😐 🙁 😠

rate your week!

/ 10

😃 😊 😐 🙁 😠

monday

hours: _____

quality: _____

wake up mood:

😀 😍 😐 🙁 😣

tuesday

hours: _____

quality: _____

wake up mood:

😀 😍 😐 🙁 😣

wednesday

hours: _____

quality: _____

wake up mood:

😀 😍 😐 🙁 😣

thursday

hours: _____

quality: _____

wake up mood:

😀 😍 😐 🙁 😣

friday

hours: _____

quality: _____

wake up mood:

😀 😍 😐 🙁 😣

saturday

hours: _____

quality: _____

wake up mood:

😀 😍 😐 🙁 😣

sunday

hours: _____

quality: _____

wake up mood:

😀 😍 😐 🙁 😣

rate your week!

/10

😀 😍 😐 🙁 😣

monday

hours: _____

quality: _____

wake up mood:

😃 😊 😐 🙁 😠

tuesday

hours: _____

quality: _____

wake up mood:

😃 😍 😐 🙁 😠

wednesday

hours: _____

quality: _____

wake up mood:

😃 😊 😐 🙁 😠

thursday

hours: _____

quality: _____

wake up mood:

😃 😍 😐 🙁 😠

friday

hours: _____

quality: _____

wake up mood:

😃 😊 😐 🙁 😠

saturday

hours: _____

quality: _____

wake up mood:

😃 😊 😐 🙁 😠

sunday

hours: _____

quality: _____

wake up mood:

😃 😍 😐 🙁 😠

rate your week!

/ 10

😃 😍 😐 🙁 😠

monday

hours: _____

quality: _____

wake up mood:

😄 😍 😐 🙁 😣

tuesday

hours: _____

quality: _____

wake up mood:

😄 😍 😐 🙁 😣

wednesday

hours: _____

quality: _____

wake up mood:

😄 😍 😐 🙁 😣

thursday

hours: _____

quality: _____

wake up mood:

😄 😍 😐 🙁 😣

friday

hours: _____

quality: _____

wake up mood:

😄 😍 😐 🙁 😣

saturday

hours: _____

quality: _____

wake up mood:

😄 😍 😐 🙁 😣

sunday

hours: _____

quality: _____

wake up mood:

😄 😍 😐 🙁 😣

rate your week!

/ 10

😄 😍 😐 🙁 😣

monday

hours: _____

quality: _____

wake up mood:

😃 😍 😐 😞 😣

tuesday

hours: _____

quality: _____

wake up mood:

😃 😍 😐 😞 😣

wednesday

hours: _____

quality: _____

wake up mood:

😃 😍 😐 😞 😣

thursday

hours: _____

quality: _____

wake up mood:

😃 😍 😐 😞 😣

friday

hours: _____

quality: _____

wake up mood:

😃 😍 😐 😞 😣

saturday

hours: _____

quality: _____

wake up mood:

😃 😍 😐 😞 😣

sunday

hours: _____

quality: _____

wake up mood:

😃 😍 😐 😞 😣

rate your week!

/ 10

😃 😍 😐 😞 😣

monday

hours: _____

quality: _____

wake up mood:

😀 😍 😐 🙁 😠

tuesday

hours: _____

quality: _____

wake up mood:

😀 😍 😐 🙁 😠

wednesday

hours: _____

quality: _____

wake up mood:

😀 😍 😐 🙁 😠

thursday

hours: _____

quality: _____

wake up mood:

😀 😍 😐 🙁 😠

friday

hours: _____

quality: _____

wake up mood:

😀 😍 😐 🙁 😠

saturday

hours: _____

quality: _____

wake up mood:

😀 😍 😐 🙁 😠

sunday

hours: _____

quality: _____

wake up mood:

😀 😍 😐 🙁 😠

rate your week!

/ 10

😀 😍 😐 🙁 😠

Clean home/clean mind

There's so much truth in this. If your home or workspace is messy, you might find your mind is messy too. When things are cluttered and unorganised your brain naturally feels the same. There's nothing **more satisfying** than spending a day (or a week!) totally decluttering. Start with one cupboard and move to the next. **Throw out** anything you don't use or take a trip to the op-shop to donate anything that's still in good condition. Use the daily planner below to map out which areas you'll declutter and clean each day.

monday

_____
_____
_____

tuesday

_____
_____
_____

wednesday

_____
_____
_____

Pro tip: Watch *Minimalism: A Documentary About the Important Things* and *Tidying Up with Marie Kondo* for all the tidying inspiration you need!

thursday

_____
_____
_____

friday

_____
_____
_____

saturday

_____
_____
_____

sunday

_____
_____
_____

clear your life, clear your mind.

"

the first step in crafting
the life you want is to get
rid of everything you don't.
"

– Joshua Becker

Now we've spent some time working on setting up the foundations, routines and rituals to a successful life, we can get into the details. Use the following pages to map out your perfect day, hour by hour.

daily routines

example!

morning
6am-11am

	M	T	W	T	F	S	S
wake up 7am	✓	✗	✓	✓	✗	✓	✓
drink 1l of water	✗	✓	✗	✗	✓	✓	✗
go for a walk	✓	✓	✓	✓	✓	✗	✗
prepare lunch	✓	✓	✓	✓	✗	✓	✓
write to-do list	✓	✓	✗	✓	✓	✗	✓

afternoon
11am-5pm

	M	T	W	T	F	S	S
have a healthy lunch	✓	✓	✓	✓	✓	✓	✓
answer all emails	✗	✓	✗	✗	✓	✓	✗
take lunch break	✓	✓	✓	✓	✓	✓	✓
drink 1l water	✓	✓	✓	✗	✗	✓	✓
exercise/gym	✓	✓	✓	✓	✓	✗	✓

evening
5pm-11pm

	M	T	W	T	F	S	S
eat healthy dinner	✓	✗	✓	✓	✗	✓	✗
skin care routine	✗	✓	✓	✗	✓	✓	✗
wash dishes	✓	✓	✓	✓	✗	✓	✓
drink 1l water	✓	✓	✓	✓	✓	✓	✓
no wine!	✓	✓	✗	✓	✓	✓	✓

daily routines

morning
6am-11am

M	T	W	T	F	S	S

_____
_____
_____
_____
_____

afternoon
11am-5pm

M	T	W	T	F	S	S

_____
_____
_____
_____
_____

evening
5pm-11pm

M	T	W	T	F	S	S

_____
_____
_____
_____
_____

daily routines

morning
6am-11am

	M	T	W	T	F	S	S

afternoon
11am-5pm

	M	T	W	T	F	S	S

evening
5pm-11pm

	M	T	W	T	F	S	S

daily routines

morning
6am-11am

M	T	W	T	F	S	S

afternoon
11am-5pm

M	T	W	T	F	S	S

evening
5pm-11pm

M	T	W	T	F	S	S

daily routines

morning
6am–11am

M	T	W	T	F	S	S

afternoon
11am–5pm

M	T	W	T	F	S	S

evening
5pm–11pm

M	T	W	T	F	S	S

daily routines

morning
6am-11am

M	T	W	T	F	S	S

afternoon
11am-5pm

M	T	W	T	F	S	S

evening
5pm-11pm

M	T	W	T	F	S	S

daily routines

morning
6am-11am

_____
_____
_____
_____

M	T	W	T	F	S	S

afternoon
11am-5pm

_____
_____
_____
_____

M	T	W	T	F	S	S

evening
5pm-11pm

_____
_____
_____
_____

M	T	W	T	F	S	S

daily routines

morning
6am-11am

_____
_____
_____
_____
_____

M	T	W	T	F	S	S

afternoon
11am-5pm

_____
_____
_____
_____
_____

M	T	W	T	F	S	S

evening
5pm-11pm

_____
_____
_____
_____
_____

M	T	W	T	F	S	S

daily routines

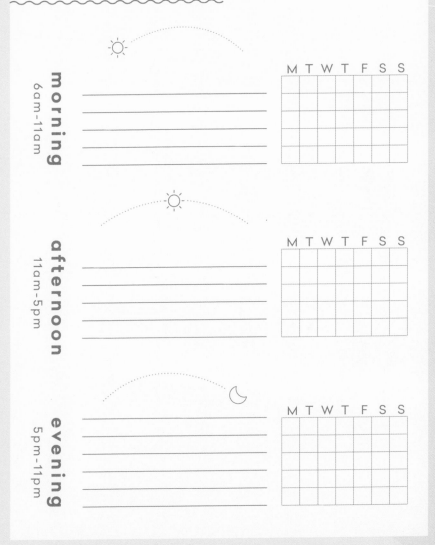

morning
6am-11am

M T W T F S S

afternoon
11am-5pm

M T W T F S S

evening
5pm-11pm

M T W T F S S

daily routines

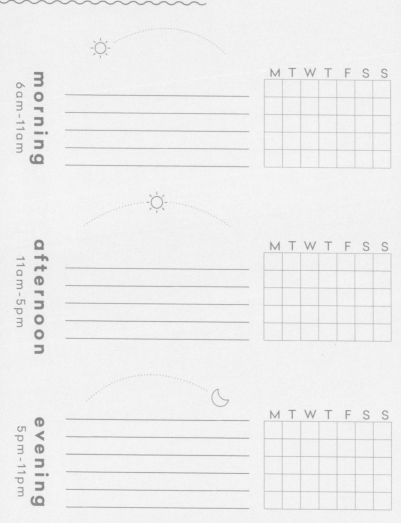

morning
6am-11am

	M	T	W	T	F	S	S

afternoon
11am-5pm

	M	T	W	T	F	S	S

evening
5pm-11pm

	M	T	W	T	F	S	S

daily routines

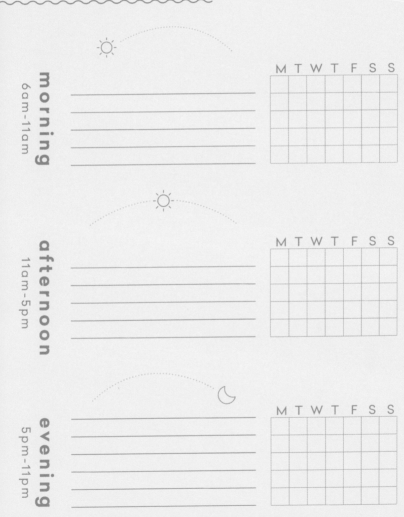

morning
6am-11am

	M	T	W	T	F	S	S

afternoon
11am-5pm

	M	T	W	T	F	S	S

evening
5pm-11pm

	M	T	W	T	F	S	S

daily routines

morning
6am-11am

M	T	W	T	F	S	S

afternoon
11am-5pm

M	T	W	T	F	S	S

evening
5pm-11pm

M	T	W	T	F	S	S

daily routines

morning
6am–11am

_____
_____
_____
_____
_____

M	T	W	T	F	S	S

afternoon
11am–5pm

_____
_____
_____
_____
_____

M	T	W	T	F	S	S

evening
5pm–11pm

_____
_____
_____
_____
_____

M	T	W	T	F	S	S

vision boards

~~~~~~~~~~~~~~~~~~

creating your very own vision board is incredibly fun, inspiring and extremely motivating! not only does it give visual reference to everything you've ever dreamed of, it magically has a way of manifesting into reality. think of all the things you want to accomplish in your life (like a bucket list) and find some old magazines and books, and cut out anything that inspires you. we also like to print pictures from websites, too – we love pinterest, it is a wonderful tool for vision boarding.

Use the next few pages to create
your very own vision boards.

Notes:

CREATE YOUR BEST LIFE

Notes:

_____
_____
_____
_____
_____
_____
_____
_____
_____
_____
_____
_____
_____
_____
_____
_____
_____
_____
_____
_____
_____
_____
_____
_____
_____
_____
_____

CREATE YOUR BEST LIFE

section three

mindset

〜〜〜〜〜〜〜〜〜〜〜〜〜〜〜〜

"

It's not how good you are,
it's how good you want to be.

" — Paul Arden

What is your mindset like? (underline the options)

positive	resilient
negative	conservative
determined	strategic
lazy	dominant
controlling	bossy
entrepreneurial	conventional
uptight	organised
anxious	competitive
analytical	ideological
methodical	cooperative
creative	collaborative
particular	technological

Write a sentence about each of the qualities you circled and why you relate to the words you circled.

_____

_____

List the best qualities about your mindset:

1. _____
2. _____
3. _____
4. _____
5. _____

List parts of your mindset that limit you:

1. _____
2. _____
3. _____
4. _____
5. _____

List the ways you can change this:

1. _____
2. _____
3. _____
4. _____
5. _____

About mindset
Fixed Mindset Vs Growth Mindset

A **fixed mindset** is the belief that people aren't capable of learning anything that they don't have a natural talent for. It assumes that intelligence and aptitude are unchanging qualities that can't be improved through learning. We think this couldn't be **further from the truth!** That's because we believe in (and encourage) a **growth mindset**.

Everything in this journal revolves around having a **growth mindset** – the belief that your talents and skills can be **developed through hard work, experience and education**. Failures aren't fatal; they're opportunities to learn, which makes people with a **growth mindset** more willing to challenge themselves. They're not worried about looking 'smart' or 'dumb' – they don't seek approval, they try different ways of learning and know that just because they haven't achieved their goals yet, doesn't mean they won't triumph eventually.

In short, you should **never feel limited** by your perceived lack of skills. Your **potential for growth is limitless**. Embrace your imperfections and get learning!

Developing a successful growth mindset
Start thinking that challenges are learning opportunities
What do you find challenging? Write down how you can turn
these into lessons:

_____
_____
_____
_____
_____
_____
_____
_____
_____

Acknowledge your imperfections and learn to love them
List ways you can leverage your imperfections and use them to
your advantage:

_____
_____
_____
_____
_____
_____
_____
_____
_____

Know your strengths and play on them
What are your strongest qualities? Write down how they will help
you achieve your dream life:

_____
_____
_____
_____
_____
_____
_____

(To delve further into finding your purpose, we suggest checking out
Lisa Messenger's *Purpose* book, available from www.lisamessenger.com)

Enjoy the process, not the end result
At what stages will you stop, reflect and digest what you've learned?

_____
_____
_____
_____
_____
_____
_____
_____
_____

Celebrate small wins
Lots of small wins equal big wins! How will you reward yourself for accomplishing those smaller goals?

_____
_____
_____
_____
_____
_____
_____
_____

Take criticism constructively

Feedback isn't always welcome, but the more you practise accepting it constructively, the easier it will be to receive. Listen to people and be accountable for your actions. List some strategies you can use to receive criticism well:

1. _____
_____
_____
_____

2. _____
_____
_____
_____

3. _____
_____
_____
_____

4. _____
_____
_____
_____

5. _____
_____
_____
_____

Ask questions and learn from everyone

It doesn't matter if the person is old, young or somebody who has nothing in common with you; **everybody holds valuable information** or experience that you can learn from. List the people you'd like to learn something from. Once you've spoken with them, include a sentence on what they taught you.

Name: _____

What did you learn?
_____
_____
_____
_____

Name: _____

What did you learn?
_____
_____
_____
_____

Name: _____

What did you learn?
_____
_____
_____
_____

Name: _____

What did you learn?

_____

_____

_____

_____

Name: _____

What did you learn?

_____

_____

_____

_____

Name: _____

What did you learn?

_____

_____

_____

_____

Name: _____

What did you learn?

_____

_____

_____

Remember to reflect

It's easy to get caught up in the moment and push on without thinking about what you've done, where you've been or what you've learnt. Remember to take **10 minutes** every couple of hours to be in the moment and process what you're doing. At the end of each day, week, month and year, **reflect** on your highs and your lows and appreciate every minute between.

Take a moment to reflect on last week and write down any words that come to mind:

_____
_____
_____
_____
_____
_____
_____
_____
_____
_____
_____
_____
_____
_____
_____
_____
_____
_____
_____

The skill I need to develop: _____

How I'm going to achieve this: _____
_____
_____

When I'm going to start: _____

The skill I need to develop: _____

How I'm going to achieve this: _____
_____
_____

When I'm going to start: _____

The skill I need to develop: _____

How I'm going to achieve this: _____
_____
_____

When I'm going to start: _____

Notes: _____
_____
_____
_____

The skill I need to develop: _____

How I'm going to achieve this: _____
_____
_____

When I'm going to start: _____

The skill I need to develop: _____

How I'm going to achieve this: _____
_____
_____

When I'm going to start: _____

The skill I need to develop: _____

How I'm going to achieve this: _____
_____
_____

When I'm going to start: _____

Notes: _____
_____
_____
_____

The skill I need to develop: _____

How I'm going to achieve this: _____
_____
_____

When I'm going to start: _____

The skill I need to develop: _____

How I'm going to achieve this: _____
_____
_____

When I'm going to start: _____

The skill I need to develop: _____

How I'm going to achieve this: _____
_____
_____

When I'm going to start: _____

Notes: _____
_____
_____
_____

if you fall, dust yourself off and try again.

"

how much you can learn
when you fail determines
how far you will go into
achieving your goals.

"

– Roy Bennett

Make goals, big and small, and track them consistently
Big things happen when you're diligent, determined and have
unwavering confidence. You have all the tools in this journal to
achieve your dreams, so what steps will you take to keep yourself
accountable in smashing those goals? List them here:

1. _____

2. _____

3. _____

4. _____

5. _____

6. _____

7. _____

8. _____

9. _____

10. _____

11. _____

12. _____

Take responsibility for your actions

Sometimes, under stressful circumstances (we all have them!) we can act out and hurt the feelings of others or make mistakes we're not happy about. The most important thing you can do in these situations is to **take responsibility**, own up, **apologise** and move onwards and upwards! List some moments in your life when you could have dealt with situations better by fessing up:

_____

_____

_____

_____

_____

_____

_____

_____

How would you treat these situations differently now?

_____

_____

_____

_____

_____

_____

_____

_____

_____

Hold yourself accountable

At the end of the day, you're the only one who's going to truly make your dreams come true. So, if you're serious, **you'll hold yourself accountable** in every step of the way. Continuously remind yourself how **amazing, strong and capable** you are. You've got this!

List some ways you can check in with yourself:

1. _____

2. _____

3. _____

4. _____

5. _____

6. _____

7. _____

8. _____

9. _____

10. _____

11. _____

12. _____

Notes:

_____

_____

_____

_____

_____

_____

_____

_____

_____

_____

_____

_____

_____

_____

_____

_____

_____

_____

_____

_____

_____

_____

_____

_____

_____

66

I am in competition with no one. I run my own race. I have no desire to play the game of being better than anyone, in any way, shape or form. I just aim to improve, to be better than I was before. That's me and I'm free.

99 — *Jenny G. Perry*

Notes:

CREATE YOUR BEST LIFE

Notes:

_____
_____
_____
_____
_____
_____
_____
_____
_____
_____
_____
_____
_____
_____
_____
_____
_____
_____
_____
_____
_____
_____
_____
_____
_____
_____
_____
_____
_____
_____

CREATE YOUR BEST LIFE

section four

comfort zones

> **"**
>
> *It's been pretty incredible to see what happens when you start believing you are enough.*
>
> **"**
>
> — *Meghan Markle*

66

Give yourself permission to live a big life. Step into who you are meant to be. Stop playing small. You're meant for greater things.

99   — Anon

What's a comfort zone?

Your comfort zone is an emotional, psychological and behavioural state where you feel safe. Life is pretty easy when you're in your comfort zone. If you're not pushing yourself, learning new things or testing your boundaries, there's nothing to stress about, right? The only issue is, when you're in your comfort zone there's not much room for **growth and development**. Stepping outside your comfort zone can be challenging and daunting, but this is where the **real magic** happens. The trick is to take things gradually and plan out your journey step-by-step. We'll show you how in the following pages.

Why you should break out of your comfort zone

Change is easier to handle

As you grow, the world around you changes and so do you. Sometimes that change isn't welcome and it can cause unwanted stress. If you practise leaving your comfort zone (in a controlled manner) then these changes can become easier to manage. The more practised you are at **pushing yourself**, the more comfortable you are with being uncomfortable, and eventually, you'll learn to embrace change and realise that most of the time **it's for the better.**

You become more creative

Taking on new challenges and experiences puts your brain into a new state of thinking. When you're in a situation you haven't been in before, you're forced to look at problems from different angles. Your brain will naturally devise **creative solutions** to help you get to the other side and out of the situation safely. When your body is experiencing some anxiety or stress you're often more productive and can **achieve more than you imagine**. The trick is to find that 'sweet spot', because we all know too much anxiety and stress causes more harm than good!

You'll become more mindful and intentional
Pushing your boundaries means you need to work out a strategy for how you will overcome a challenge. This will inevitably require a lot of thinking and doing. Forcing yourself to break out of your comfort zone will require mindfulness and controlled thinking, so you don't get too stressed. There will be moments where you need to pause, **catch your breath and pep-talk yourself**. Having an open mind will help with re-aligning your visions.

You'll see how resilient you really are
We're not going to lie to you, there will be tough times. These challenges can be confronting and uncomfortable, but you'll find a way to work through it and the experience will make you **stronger than ever**. Resilience is powerful and once you have it, **you'll be unstoppable!**

Notes:

_____
_____
_____
_____
_____
_____
_____
_____
_____
_____
_____
_____

Three foolproof ways you can get out of your comfort zone

1. Research what scares you
Sometimes we simply fear things because we aren't educated enough about them. Take the time to do some research, learn as much as you can before making the leap. The more you know about your fear, the more you'll feel prepared to face the challenge.

List five things that terrify you:

1. _____

2. _____

3. _____

4. _____

5. _____

How will you conquer these fears?

_____
_____
_____
_____
_____
_____
_____
_____
_____

2. Take baby steps

One step at a time is probably the best advice you can receive at this point. Everyone starts somewhere and so long as you're taking action, you're well on your way. Remember that even set-backs and failures are learning curves and are important steps in moving forward. List five set-backs you've had:

1. _____

2. _____

3. _____

4. _____

5. _____

What are the lessons you learned from them?

_____
_____
_____
_____
_____
_____
_____
_____
_____
_____
_____
_____
_____
_____

3. Take a trusty companion with you

Having a friend or someone you trust by your side can encourage you to break through your safety net. Everything is a little easier when you have support and guidance. Pick and choose your 'people' carefully. You might like to buddy up with someone who has already done what you want to achieve and ask them to mentor you through it. Or, you may just need someone to provide you with moral support. Don't feel like you need to embark on any challenges alone.

List 10 people you consider **trustworthy companions** to break down comfort zones with:

1. _____

2. _____

3. _____

4. _____

5. _____

6. _____

7. _____

8. _____

9. _____

10. _____

"

if you wish to move
mountains tomorrow,
you must start by lifting
stones today.

"

– African proverb

two-week challenge
breaking the ice

day 1:
say "yes" to
everything

day 2:
spark a conversation
with a stranger (a real
conversation!)

day 3:
switch off your
phone and get in
touch with reality

day 4:
contact
someone who
inspires you

day 5:
do something
that really
scares you

day 6:
wake up earlier
and go for a
walk/run

day 7:
speak about your dreams
with a trusted friend

day 8:
ask for some
constructive
criticism

day 9:
switch up
your routine

day 10:
give up control –
hand something
you care about over
to somebody else

day 11:
take up a
new hobby
or sport

day 12:
sign yourself up
for a workshop
or short course

day 13:
let go of anything
that's holding you
back (including
friends)

day 14:
continue to
push yourself
out of your
comfort zone!

When it all gets a bit too much

It's normal to feel overwhelmed and anxious when you're stepping into something new. Sometimes it can all get just a bit too much to handle, and that's OK! When these moments happen, it's important to know some **coping strategies** so you can take a big deep breath, reconcile, reflect and reset. Over the next few pages we'll help you with different strategies to **calm yourself down** and get back into the flow of **achieving your goals.**

Understand your triggers

Know what types of things can set you off. These can be situations, sounds, personalities, workloads, deadlines, controversy, health challenges and more. What negative triggers affect you the most?

1. _____

2. _____

3. _____

4. _____

5. _____

6. _____

7. _____

8. _____

CREATE YOUR BEST LIFE

Now that you're more aware of your triggers, try to limit these in your life. However, sometimes we just can't avoid them. In these instances, use them as an opportunity to work through them on your own terms, in a controlled and calm manner.

Notes:

_____

_____

_____

_____

_____

_____

_____

_____

_____

_____

_____

_____

_____

_____

_____

_____

_____

_____

_____

5 ways to self-soothe using your five senses

touch
have something super-soft to run your hands over, or keep a stress ball handy.

hear
engage with all the noises around you, list them all in your head and then separate each sound and focus on only that sound for 10 to 20 seconds. repeat this step three times.

see
look around you and note everything you can see. linger on a specific object for 10 seconds and note all the details, then move to the next – do this for five different objects.

taste
if available, make yourself a cup of herbal tea or prepare a healthy snack. take your mind off the situation and replace it with another more calming action.

smell
breathe in and pinpoint any scents that fill the air around you. focus on this for 20 seconds.

> ❝
> *The comeback is always*
> *stronger than the setback.*
>
> ❞
> — Unknown

once you've been through all five senses you
should notice a huge difference in how you
feel. just taking your mind off the situation
completely and then revisiting later can make
the whole experience much more manageable.

40 ways to calm down

take five deep breaths

go for a walk

draw a picture

practise yoga

exercise

drink herbal tea (camomile is best!)

read a book

call a friend

stretch

change into comfy clothes

have a hot shower/bath

get a massage

light some candles

listen to calming music

write about a happy time in your life

do a crossword

visit your local library

journal about your day

tidy the house

buy fresh flowers

go for a swim in the ocean

spend time
with a pet/animal

cook a new dish

meditate

take a 30-minute
nap or rest

dream a little

spend time with
a loved one

turn off your phone

take yourself out
for lunch

have a complete
rest day

declutter your
wardrobe

write about your
negative thoughts
then throw them
in the bin

do something kind

play a board game

use aromatherapy

write down 10 things
you're grateful for

do some housework

visualise a peaceful
place

take yourself out
for a coffee

play your
favourite music
and dance!

Notes:

_____
_____
_____
_____
_____
_____
_____
_____
_____
_____
_____
_____
_____
_____
_____
_____
_____
_____
_____
_____
_____
_____
_____
_____
_____

Notes:

_____
_____
_____
_____
_____
_____
_____
_____
_____
_____
_____
_____
_____
_____
_____
_____
_____
_____
_____
_____
_____
_____
_____
_____
_____
_____
_____
_____
_____

creating a success persona

> **"**
>
> *"Be relentless.*
> *Be ambitious.*
> *Be excellent."*
>
> **"**
> — Roxane Gay

66

Apply for that job.
Date that person.
Buy that plane ticket.
Move to that city.
Do all the things that scare you,
because they're worth it.

99   — *Anon*

Now that you know exactly what you need to do to create your dream life, it's time to begin actually living it. Think up a person who you would **aspire to be**, somebody who is living your complete dream life. Think about everything that is in their life and how they got to be where they are now. Fill out the questions below to create your success persona.

Where does this person live?

_____

_____

_____

_____

_____

_____

_____

What kind of house do they have?

_____

_____

_____

_____

_____

_____

_____

_____

_____

_____

What career are they in?

_____
_____
_____
_____
_____
_____

What is their job title?

_____
_____
_____
_____
_____

What gives them the most joy?

_____
_____
_____
_____
_____
_____
_____
_____
_____

What drives them to succeed?

_____

_____

_____

_____

_____

_____

Where do they take holidays?

_____

_____

_____

_____

_____

_____

What countries do they visit?

_____

_____

_____

_____

_____

_____

CREATE YOUR BEST LIFE

What does a day in their life look like?

7am: _____

8am: _____

9am: _____

10am: _____

11am: _____

12pm: _____

1pm: _____

2pm: _____

3pm: _____

4pm: _____

5pm: _____

6pm: _____

7pm: _____

8pm: _____

What is their health like?

_____
_____
_____
_____
_____
_____

What do they eat in a day?

_____
_____
_____
_____
_____
_____

Who are their mentors?

1. _____
2. _____
3. _____
4. _____
5. _____
6. _____
7. _____
8. _____
9. _____
10. _____

What is their personality like?

_____
_____
_____
_____
_____
_____
_____

How do they take care of themselves?

_____
_____
_____
_____
_____
_____
_____

What are their spending habits?

_____
_____
_____
_____
_____
_____

Notes:

_____
_____
_____
_____
_____
_____
_____
_____
_____
_____
_____
_____
_____
_____
_____
_____
_____
_____
_____
_____
_____
_____
_____
_____
_____
_____
_____
_____
_____
_____
_____

CREATE YOUR BEST LIFE

create a plan to live the life
of your success persona

dot point your strategy:

-
-
-
-
-
-
-
-
-
-
-
-

moodboard

draw/journal

Notes:

_____
_____
_____
_____
_____
_____
_____
_____
_____
_____
_____
_____
_____
_____
_____
_____
_____
_____
_____
_____
_____
_____
_____
_____
_____

CREATE YOUR BEST LIFE

section

six

accountability planner

Believe in your infinite potential. Your only limitations are those you set upon yourself.

— Rey T. Bennett

> **"**
>
> *All mistakes teach us*
> *something, so there*
> *are, in reality, no*
> *mistakes. Just things*
> *we learn.*
>
> **"**
>
> — *Nikki Giovanni*

week one

Now that you've analysed every detail of your dream life and know exactly what you need to do to get out of your comfort zone, it's time for you to put a solid plan in place, map out your goals and **remain accountable**. Use the next few pages to keep your dream life plan on track and your mindset in check. **Time to smash some goals!**

The week ahead
My goal for this week is:

_____
_____
_____

I will work toward my goal for this week by:

_____
_____
_____

I think I will struggle with:

_____
_____
_____

What I think I will find the easiest:

_____
_____
_____

Five things I want to focus on this week are:

1. _____

_____

_____

_____

2. _____

_____

_____

_____

_____

3. _____

_____

_____

_____

_____

4. _____

_____

_____

_____

_____

5. _____

_____

_____

_____

_____

Something I'd like to improve:

_____
_____
_____

Something I'd like to let go of:

_____
_____
_____

My notes for the week:

_____
_____
_____
_____
_____
_____
_____
_____
_____
_____
_____
_____
_____
_____

write a quote that sums up this week

The week in reflection
Did I achieve my goal? If so, how:

_____
_____
_____

If not, how will I work toward achieving it next week?

_____
_____
_____

What I found difficult:

_____
_____
_____

What I found easy:

_____
_____
_____

What I'm most proud of:

_____
_____
_____

Five reasons I'm grateful for the past week:

1. _____
   _____
   _____

2. _____
   _____
   _____

3. _____
   _____
   _____

4. _____
   _____
   _____

5. _____
   _____
   _____

Something I'd like to improve:

_____

Something I'd like to let go of:

_____
_____

week two

The week ahead
My goal for this week is:

_____
_____
_____
_____

I will work toward my goal for this week by:

_____
_____
_____
_____

I think I will struggle with:

_____
_____
_____
_____

What I think I will find the easiest:

_____
_____
_____
_____

CREATE YOUR BEST LIFE

Five things I want to focus on this week:

1. _____
   _____
   _____
   _____

2. _____
   _____
   _____
   _____
   _____

3. _____
   _____
   _____
   _____
   _____

4. _____
   _____
   _____
   _____
   _____

5. _____
   _____
   _____
   _____
   _____

Something I'd like to improve:

_____
_____
_____

Something I'd like to let go of:

_____
_____
_____

My notes for the week:

_____
_____
_____
_____
_____
_____
_____
_____
_____
_____
_____
_____
_____

write a quote that sums up this week

The week in reflection
Did I achieve my goal? If so, how:

_____
_____
_____

If not, how will I work toward achieving it next week?

_____
_____
_____

What I found difficult:

_____
_____
_____

What I found easy:

_____
_____
_____

What I'm most proud of:

_____
_____
_____

Five reasons I'm grateful for the past week:

1. _____
_____
_____

2. _____
_____
_____

3. _____
_____
_____

4. _____
_____
_____

5. _____
_____

Something I'd like to improve:

_____

Something I'd like to let go of:

_____
_____

week three

The week ahead
My goal for this week is:

_____
_____
_____
_____

I will work toward my goal for this week by:

_____
_____
_____
_____

I think I will struggle with:

_____
_____
_____
_____

What I think I will find the easiest:

_____
_____
_____
_____

CREATE YOUR BEST LIFE

Five things I want to focus on this week:

1. _____
_____
_____
_____

2. _____
_____
_____
_____
_____

3. _____
_____
_____
_____
_____

4. _____
_____
_____
_____
_____

5. _____
_____
_____
_____
_____

Something I'd like to improve:

_____
_____
_____

Something I'd like to let go of:

_____
_____
_____

My notes for the week:

_____
_____
_____
_____
_____
_____
_____
_____
_____
_____
_____
_____
_____
_____

write a quote that sums up this week

The week in reflection
Did I achieve my goal? If so, how:

_____
_____
_____

If not, how will I work toward achieving it next week?

_____
_____
_____

What I found difficult:

_____
_____
_____

What I found easy:

_____
_____
_____

What I'm most proud of:

_____
_____
_____

Five reasons I'm grateful for the past week:

1. _____
_____
_____

2. _____
_____
_____

3. _____
_____
_____

4. _____
_____
_____

5. _____
_____
_____

Something I'd like to improve:

_____

Something I'd like to let go of:

_____
_____

week four

The week ahead

My goal for this week is:

_____
_____
_____
_____

I will work toward my goal for this week by:

_____
_____
_____
_____

I think I will struggle with:

_____
_____
_____
_____

What I think I will find the easiest:

_____
_____
_____
_____

Five things I want to focus on this week:

1. _____
_____
_____
_____

2. _____
_____
_____
_____
_____

3. _____
_____
_____
_____
_____

4. _____
_____
_____
_____
_____

5. _____
_____
_____
_____
_____

Something I'd like to improve:

_____
_____
_____

Something I'd like to let go of:

_____
_____
_____

My notes for the week:

_____
_____
_____
_____
_____
_____
_____
_____
_____
_____
_____
_____
_____
_____
_____

write a quote that sums up this week

The week in reflection
Did I achieve my goal? If so, how:

_____
_____
_____

If not, how will I work toward achieving it next week?

_____
_____
_____

What I found difficult:

_____
_____
_____

What I found easy:

_____
_____
_____

What I'm most proud of:

_____
_____
_____

Five reasons I'm grateful for the past week:

1. _____
_____
_____

2. _____
_____
_____

3. _____
_____
_____

4. _____
_____
_____

5. _____
_____
_____

Something I'd like to improve:

_____

Something I'd like to let go of:

_____
_____

constantly choose your best life.

if it's not
working
for you, be
unafraid
to change.

Accountability in reflection

Congratulations, you've completed a full month of holding yourself accountable to your goals! How did you go? Did you manage to achieve everything you set your mind on? Whatever you managed, you're much closer to living your dream life than when you started. Now is the time to **reflect on the past month** and what you found comfortable, challenging, overwhelming or a walk in the park. Spend some time journaling about your experience over the next few pages.

_____
_____
_____
_____
_____
_____
_____
_____
_____
_____
_____
_____
_____
_____
_____
_____
_____
_____
_____
_____
_____
_____

CREATE YOUR BEST LIFE

section seven

mindfulness

Nothing can stop the man with the right mental attitude from achieving his goal; nothing on earth can help the man with the wrong mental attitude.

— Thomas Jefferson

"

Trust the wait.
Embrace the uncertainty.
Enjoy the beauty of becoming.
When nothing is certain,
anything is possible.

"   — Anon

We touched on mindfulness in earlier sections of this journal, but let's delve a little deeper. Being in a state of mindfulness positively affects people's **ability to achieve** personal goals, allows for greater levels of **independence** and assists with increasing general **wellbeing.** Those who practise mindfulness regularly appear to be happier, more relaxed, focused and more present in everyday situations. In comparison, people who don't practise mindfulness can feel more stressed, anxious, impulsive and have less control over their moods. **So, how exactly can we practise mindfulness?**

1. Get an app! Guided mindful meditations are a perfect way to start.

2. Let go. Stop judging yourself and, more importantly, others.

3. Accept thoughts as they come and go; acknowledge them and then let them slip away.

4. Be quiet. Find some time and space to just be.

5. Consider every action in every aspect of your life.

6. Practise yoga regularly.

7. Open your heart. Practise: "I am good, I do good and I am loved."

8. Experience every moment. Put that device down!

9. Be present. Engage in real, authentic, true conversations.

10. Accept where you are. Every stage in life is happening for a reason.

List some ways that you already practise mindfulness:

1. _____
_____
_____
_____
_____

2. _____
_____
_____
_____
_____

3. _____
_____
_____
_____
_____

4. _____
_____
_____
_____
_____

5. _____
_____
_____
_____
_____

How can you be more mindful?

_____
_____
_____
_____
_____
_____

List your limitations with practising mindfulness:

1. _____

2. _____

3. _____

4. _____

5. _____

How can you overcome these?

_____
_____
_____
_____
_____

a little peace and quiet does wonders for the soul.

10-minute mindfulness
meditation challenge

here, we've mapped out an easy meditation for you to follow. try to do this every day for a week and notice how you feel after you complete each practice. journal your experience in the following pages.

time
choose a time each day to complete your mindfulness meditation. slowly build from five minutes up to 15 or 20 minutes.

take five deep breaths
realise where you are and breathe comfort into the space where you're sitting. establish your mental state for a positive meditation experience.

space
find a space where you're away from distraction and you can sit quietly for the duration of your practice.

get comfortable
ideally, sit cross-legged or in an upright chair with your feet flat on the ground.

check your posture
be aware of how your back, neck and shoulders are sitting. realign and reset if you've begun to slouch.

direct your attention to breathing

take deep breaths in and out through your nose, focus on the feeling of it coming in and out of your body. imagine fresh air floating in, and old air coming out.

maintain attention on your breathing

as you inhale and exhale, try to maintain the focus on your breathing. if your mind wanders, that's ok. acknowledge the thought, let it go and come back to your breath.

direct attention to noises around you

pinpoint one noise to focus on, sit with it, listen to it and then pick another sound to focus on. repeat this step for two minutes.

direct attention to smells around you

pinpoint one smell to focus on, sit with it, breathe it in, establish what it is and picture how it looks. repeat this step for two minutes.

give gratitude

think about five things you're grateful for, one at a time. spend a moment on each and appreciate why you're giving gratitude to this particular thing.

allow yourself time to come out of your meditation

don't rush. be mindful and carry these thoughts with you until your next practice.

be easeful
and find
peace in
whichever
direction
life takes
you.

have
faith in
the future
and learn
to go
with the
flow.

@collectivehub

Day 1:
Circle the face that is most relevant to your practice today.

😖 🙁 🙂 😐 😲 😊 😌 😄

Notes:

_____

_____

_____

_____

_____

_____

_____

Day 2:
Circle the face that is most relevant to your practice today.

😖 🙁 🙂 😐 😲 😊 😌 😄

Notes:

_____

_____

_____

_____

_____

_____

_____

Day 3:
Circle the face that is most relevant to your practice today.

😣 😟 😕 😐 😧 🙂 😊 😄

Notes:

_____
_____
_____
_____
_____
_____
_____

Day 4:
Circle the face that is most relevant to your practice today.

😣 😟 😕 😐 😧 🙂 😊 😄

Notes:

_____
_____
_____
_____
_____
_____
_____

Day 5:
Circle the face that is most relevant to your practice today.

😖 😟 🙂 😐 😲 🙂 😊 😃

Notes:

_____
_____
_____
_____
_____
_____
_____

Day 6:
Circle the face that is most relevant to your practice today.

😖 😟 🙂 😐 😲 🙂 😊 😃

Notes:

_____
_____
_____
_____
_____
_____
_____

Day 7:
Circle the face that is most relevant to your practice today.

😖 😞 😟 😐 😨 🙂 😊 😃

Notes:

_____
_____
_____
_____
_____
_____
_____

Write your thoughts and reflections after your week of practising mindful meditations:

_____
_____
_____
_____
_____
_____
_____
_____
_____
_____
_____
_____
_____

Notes:

CREATE YOUR BEST LIFE

Notes:

_____
_____
_____
_____
_____
_____
_____
_____
_____
_____
_____
_____
_____
_____
_____
_____
_____
_____
_____
_____
_____
_____
_____
_____
_____
_____

CREATE YOUR BEST LIFE

section eight

hard work & determination

> 66
>
> *Success doesn't come from*
> *what you do occasionally,*
> *it comes from what you*
> *do consistently.*
>
> 99 — Marie Forleo

"

Be brave.
Take risks.
Nothing can
substitute
experience.

" — *Paulo Coelho*

You'll know by now that the dream life doesn't just come served on a silver platter. In order for you to truly gain what you want, you need to put the hard work and effort in. Personal growth takes time, determination and a lot of resilience. Things won't always go your way and there will be moments of failure. How you resurface and learn from these challenges will be the greatest moments of self development and bring you closer to living your ultimate dream life. Remember to keep yourself accountable and continue to use the previous pages to keep yourself in check and gradually tick off your goals.

How to stay determined

Sometimes it can be hard to keep carrying on. You'll question yourself a lot and you might feel like going back to your original, uninspiring routine. **This is just a phase!** The best thing to do is step away, go for a walk and **remember why you started this in the first place**. If you're feeling a lull in your energy try some of these techniques to get back on track.

1. **Acknowledge your progress** – it's OK if you're a little slow, progress is progress!

2. **Surround yourself with positivity** – including people!

3. **Believe in yourself** – you can do it!

4. **Quit procrastinating** – sometimes you just need to force yourself back in.

5. **Set realistic goals** – remember, one step at a time.

6. **Daydream a little** – but stay focused on your immediate goals.

7. **Push through fear** – 20 seconds of courage is all you need.

8. **Give yourself credit** – look how far you've already come.

9. **Realign your vision, if necessary** – be flexible with uncontrollable factors.

10. **Visualise and manifest** – if you believe it, you can do it.

When it comes, know your strategy
Forecast how and when you might feel a bump in your journey.

How will you work through it? List 12 ways that you can help yourself through and get back on track:

1. _____

2. _____

3. _____

4. _____

5. _____

6. _____

7. _____

8. _____

9. _____

10. _____

11. _____

12. _____

Get help if you need it

Set your intentions from the beginning and voice your goals and dreams to those closest around you. Don't be afraid to reach for help if you need it. Maybe you're using this journal to start a new business, or embark on an overseas adventure. Whatever it is, **get the help you need**. It might be an extra set of hands to help with odd jobs around the house, or perhaps it's somebody to help you manage your admin, or help book your flights. You'll be surprised at how much people will want to see you achieve your dreams and naturally reach out to help.

What are some things you will need help with?

1. _____

2. _____

3. _____

4. _____

Who will you ask to help you when the time comes?

1. _____

2. _____

3. _____

4. _____

love yourself again

list all the things that inspire you and give you energy to pursue your dreams:

1. _____

2. _____

3. _____

4. _____

5. _____

6. _____

7. _____

8. _____

9. _____

10. _____

11. _____

12. _____

inspirational resources
we love

pinterest

tedtalks

books

conferences

blogs

motivational
quotes

podcasts

audiobooks

journals

social
platforms

industry
leaders

mentors

netflix

documentaries

medium.com

audible.com

magazines

news outlets

mother nature

ebooks
and zines

And finally, remember 'why'

Why are you here? Why are you doing this?

Ask yourself this often. Whenever you're feeling a little bit disheartened or disengaged from your plans, remind yourself **why you started in the first place**. This should be the biggest motivator to get you back in the zone.

So, why?

_____

_____

_____

_____

_____

_____

_____

_____

_____

_____

_____

_____

_____

_____

_____

_____

_____

_____

_____

_____

Congratulations!

You've made it to the end of our *Best Life Journal*. We hope you've designed your best life, in the best way possible, by using all our tools, actions, advices and knowledge throughout these pages.

From wherever you've come from and to wherever you're going, we hope you implement your learnings and go forth and conquer. Remember to push forward with a clear vision, wild imagination and strong intensions. Walk boldly, explore courageously, think mindfully, throw away your negative thoughts and most importantly, be true to yourself and your dreams, goals and visions. Whoever you are, we believe in you — you can do it!

journaling

moodboarding

make today
the day you
discover
your light!

step into
your power
and change
the game.

make all your thoughts positive and empowering. you've got this!

fin·

365 DOSES OF INSPIRING WISDOM

Daily mantras to ignite your purpose

TO LIVE YOUR BEST AND BRAVEST LIFE

LISA MESSENGER

FOUNDER AND EDITOR-IN-CHIEF OF *COLLECTIVE HUB*

Learn from yesterday. Cherish today.
Dream big for tomorrow.

Thoughtfully curated by entrepreneur,
author and speaker Lisa Messenger,
these artfully presented quotes can be
used as meditations, as musings, or as
your daily dose of inspiration; one
for each day of the year. Every daily
message includes a quote, followed by
Lisa's personal take, and an affirmation
that will help you to step into and
ground your courage, spirit, wisdom
and wit that make every day count.

Buy your copy today
www.collectivehub.com

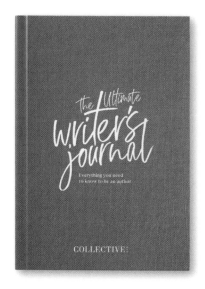

Love this journal?
Purchase our Ultimate Writer's Journal to
kickstart your writing passions and get published!

Or, travelling soon? Our Ultimate Travel Journal
will be the perfect companion on your journey.

Available from
www.collectivehub.com

Collect all of
Lisa Messenger's books!
Buy your copy at
www.collectivehub.com

Want to secure a back issue of *Collective Hub*
magazine? Jump online at www.collectivehub.com
to see our full catalogue and order yours today.